TOMMY AND THE WISHING-STONE

Mother Grouse knew there were dangers
on every side

Tommy and the Wishing-Stone

By

THORNTON W. BURGESS

ILLUSTRATED BY
HARRISON CADY

PUBLISHERS

Grosset & Dunlap

NEW YORK

To the cause of love, mercy, and protection for our little friends of the air and the wildwood, and to a better understanding of them, the Wishing-Stone Stories are dedicated.

Tommy and the Wishing-Stone

CONTENTS

———

CHAPTER

I   Tommy and the Wishing-Stone .   1

II   How Tommy Learned to Admire
Thunderer the Ruffed Grouse   25

III   What Happened When
Tommy Became a Mink . . .   55

IV   Tommy Becomes a Very
Humble Person   81

ILLUSTRATIONS

Mother Grouse knew there were dangers on every side . . . . FRONTISPIECE

Blacky the Crow   1

He loved to hear the bees humming and the birds singing 22

Bugs were to be found under old logs 38

Out popped the brown head of Mrs. Mink 64

When he was feeling lazy, he would catch a frog 74

Tommy saw them sitting upright in the shallow water 94

"Toad weather! Perfect Toad weather!" exclaimed old Mr. Toad 95

TOMMY AND THE WISHING-STONE

Blacky the Crow

CHAPTER ONE

TOMMY AND THE WISHING-STONE

TOMMY scuffed his bare, brown feet in the grass and didn't even notice how cooling and refreshing to his bare toes the green blades were. Usually he just loved to feel them, but this afternoon he just didn't want to find anything pleasant or nice in the things he was accustomed to. A scowl, a deep, dark, heavy scowl, had chased all merriment from his round, freckled face. It seemed as if the very freckles were trying to hide from it.

Tommy didn't care. He said so. He said so right out loud. He didn't care if all the world knew it. He wanted the world to know it. It was a horrid old world anyway, this world which made a fellow go hunt up and drive home a lot of pesky cows just when all the other fellows were over at the swimming-hole. It always was that way whenever there was anything interesting or particular to do, or any fun going on. Yes, it was a horrid old world, this world in which Tommy lived, and he was quite willing that everybody should know it.

The truth was, Tommy was deep, very deep, in the sulks. He was so deep in them that he couldn't see jolly round Mr. Sun smiling down on him. He couldn't see anything lovely in the beautiful, broad, Green Meadows with the shadows of the clouds chasing one another across them. He couldn't hear the music of the birds and the bees. He couldn't even hear the Merry Little Breezes whispering secrets as they danced around him. He couldn't see and hear because — well, because he *wouldn't* see and hear. That is always the way with people who go way down deep in the sulks.

Presently he came to a great big stone. Tommy stopped and scowled at it just as he had been scowling at everybody and everything. He scowled at it as if he thought it had no business to be there. Yet all the time he was glad that it was there. It was just the right size to sit on and try to make himself happy by being perfectly miserable. You know, some people actually find pleasure in thinking how miserable they are. The more miserable they can make themselves feel, the sooner they begin to pity themselves, and when they begin to pity themselves they seem to find what Uncle Jason calls a "melancholy pleasure."

It was that way with Tommy. Because no one else seemed to pity him, he wanted to pity himself, and to do that right he must first make himself feel the most miserable he possibly could. So he sat down on the big stone, waved his stick for a few moments and then threw it away, put his chin in his two hands and his two elbows on his two knees, and began by scowling down at his bare, brown toes.

"There's never anything to do around

here, and when there is, a fellow can't do it," he grumbled. "Other fellows don't have to weed the garden, and bring in wood, and drive the cows, and when they do it, it isn't just when they want to have some fun. What's vacation for, if it isn't to have a good time in? And how's a fellow going to do it when he has to work all the time — anyway when he has to work just when he doesn't want to?" He was trying to be truthful.

"Fellows who live in town have something going on all the time, while out here there's nothing but fields, and woods, and sky, and — and cows that haven't sense enough to come home themselves when it's time. There's never anything exciting or int'resting 'round here. I wish ——"

He suddenly became aware of two very small bright eyes watching him from a little opening in the grass. He scowled at them harder than ever, and moved ever so little. The eyes disappeared, but a minute later they were back again, full of curiosity, a little doubtful, a little fearful, but tremendously interested. They were the eyes of Danny Meadow Mouse. Tommy knew them right away. Of course he did. Hadn't he chased Danny with sticks and stones time and again? But he didn't think of this now. He was too full of his own troubles to remember that others had troubles too.

Somehow Danny's twinkling little eyes seemed to mock him. How unjust things were!

"*You* don't have to work!" he ex-

ploded so suddenly and fiercely that
Danny gave a frightened squeak and
took to his heels. "You don't have anything to do but play all day and have
a good time. I wish I was a meadow-
mouse!"

Right then and there something happened, Tommy didn't know how it happened, but it just did. Instead of a
bare-legged, freckle-faced, sulky boy sitting on the big stone, he suddenly found
himself a little, chunky, blunt-headed,
furry animal with four short legs and a
ridiculously short stubby tail. And he
was scampering after Danny Meadow
Mouse along a private little path
through the meadow-grass. He was a
meadow-mouse himself! His wish had
come true!

Tommy felt very happy. He had

forgotten that he ever was a boy. He raced along the private little path just as if he had always been accustomed to just such private little paths. It might be very hot out in the sun, but down there among the sheltering grass stems it was delightfully cool and comfortable. He tried to shout for very joy, but what he really did do was to squeak. It was a thin, sharp little squeak. It was answered right away from in front of him, and Tommy didn't like the sound of it. Being a meadow-mouse now, he understood the speech of meadow-mice, and he knew that Danny Meadow Mouse was demanding to know who was running in his private little path. Tommy suspected by the angry sound of Danny's voice that he meant to fight.

Tommy hesitated.   Then he stopped.

He didn't want to fight. You see, he knew that he had no business in that path without an invitation from the owner. If it had been his own path he would have been eager to fight. But it wasn't, and so he thought it best to avoid trouble. He turned and scampered back a little way to a tiny branch path. He followed this until it also branched, and then took the new path.

But none of these paths really belonged to him. He wanted some of his very own. Now the only way to have a private path of your very own in the Green Meadows is to make it, unless you are big enough and strong enough to take one away from some one else.

So Tommy set to work to make a path of his own, and he did it by cutting the grass one stem at a time. The very tender ones he ate. The dry ones he carried to an old board he had discovered, and under this he made a nest, using the finest, softest grasses for the inside. Of course it was work. As a matter of fact, had he, as a boy, had to work one-tenth as much or as hard as he now had to work as a meadow-mouse, he would have felt sure that he was the most abused boy who ever lived. But, being a meadow-mouse, he didn't think anything about it, and scurried back and forth as fast as ever he could, just stopping now and then to rest. He knew that he must work for everything he had—that without work he would have nothing. And somehow this all seemed perfectly right. He was busy, and in keeping busy he kept happy.

Presently, as he sat down to rest a

minute, a Merry Little Breeze came hurrying along, and brought with it just the faintest kind of a sound. It made his heart jump. Every little unexpected sound made his heart jump. He listened with all his might. There it was again! Something was stealing very, very softly through the grass. He felt sure it was danger of some kind. Then he did a foolish thing — he ran. You see, he was so frightened that he felt that he just couldn't sit still a second longer. So he ran. The instant he moved, something big and terrible sprang at him, and two great paws with sharp claws spread out all but landed on him. He gave a frightened squeak, and darted under a fallen old fencepost that lay half hidden in the tall grass.

"What's the matter with you?" demanded a voice. Tommy found that he had company. It was another meadow-mouse.

"I — I've had such a narrow escape!" panted Tommy. "A terrible creature with awful claws almost caught me!"

The stranger peeped out to see. "Pooh!" said he, "that was only a cat. Cats don't know much. If you keep your ears and eyes open, it's easy enough to fool cats. But they are a terrible nuisance, just the same, because they are always prowling around when you least expect them. I hate cats! It is bad enough to have to watch out all the time for enemies who live on the Green Meadows, without having to be always looking to see if a cat is about. A cat hasn't any excuse at all. It has all it wants to eat without trying to catch us. It hunts just out of love of cruelty. Now Reddy Fox has some excuse; he has to eat.   Too bad he's so fond of meadow-mice.   Speaking of Reddy, have you seen him lately?"

Tommy shook his head.   "I guess it's safe enough to go out now," continued the stranger.   "I know where there is a lot of dandy corn; let's go get some."

Tommy was quite willing.   The stranger led the way.   First he looked this way and that way, and listened for any sound of danger.   Tommy did like-wise.   But the way seemed clear, and away they scampered.   Right away Tommy was happy again.   He had for-gotten his recent fright.   That is the way with little people of the Green Meadows.   But he didn't forget to keep his ears and his eyes wide open for new dangers. They reached the corn safely, and then such a feast as they did have! It seemed to Tommy that never had he tasted anything half so good. Right in the midst of the feast, the stranger gave a faint little squeak and darted under a pile of old cornstalks. Tommy didn't stop to ask questions, but followed right at his heels. A big, black shadow swept over them and then passed on. Tommy peeped out. There was a great bird with huge, broad wings sailing back and forth over the meadows.

"It's old Whitetail the Marsh Hawk. He didn't get us that time!" chuckled the stranger, and crept back to the delicious corn. In two minutes, they were having as good a time as before, just as if they hadn't had a narrow escape.

When they had eaten all they could hold, the stranger went back to his old fence-post and Tommy returned to his own private paths and the snug nest he had built under the old board.   He was sleepy, and he curled up for a good long nap.

When he awoke, the first stars were beginning to twinkle down at him from the sky, and Black Shadows lay over the Green Meadows.   He found that he could see quite as well as in the light of day, and, because he was already hungry again, he started out to look for something to eat.   Something inside warned him that he must watch out for danger now just as sharply as before, though the Black Shadows seemed to promise safety.   Just what he was to watch out for he didn't know, still every few steps he stopped to look and listen.

He found that this was visiting time among the meadow-mice, and he made a great many friends. There was a great deal of scurrying back and forth along private little paths, and a great deal of squeaking. At least, that is what Tommy would have called it had he still been a boy, but as it was, he understood it perfectly, for it was meadow-mouse language. Suddenly not a sound was to be heard, not a single squeak or the sound of scurrying feet. Tommy sat perfectly still and held his breath. He didn't know why, but something inside told him to, and he did. Then something passed over him. It was like a Black Shadow, and it was just as silent as a Black Shadow.

But Tommy knew that it wasn't a Black Shadow, for out of it two great, round, fierce, yellow eyes glared down and struck such terror to his heart that it almost stopped beating.   But they didn't see him, and he gave a tiny sigh of relief as he watched the grim living shadow sail on.   While he watched, there was a frightened little squeak, two legs with great curved claws dropped down from the shadow, plunged into the grass, and when they came up again they held a little limp form.   A little mouse had moved when he shouldn't have, and Hooty the Owl had caught a dinner.

A dozen times that night Tommy sat quite frozen with fear while Hooty passed, but after each time he joined with his fellows in merry-making just as if there was no such thing as this terrible feathered hunter with the silent wings, only each one was ready to hide at the first sign of danger. When he grew tired of playing and eating, he returned to his snug nest under the old board to sleep. He was still asleep there the next morning when, without any warning, the old board was lifted. In great fright Tommy ran out of his nest, and at once there was a great shout from a huge giant, who struck at him with a stick and then chased him, throwing sticks and stones, none of which hit him, but which frightened him terribly. He dodged down a little path and ran for his life, while behind him he heard the giant (it was just a boy) shouting and laughing as he poked about in the grass trying to find poor Tommy, and Tommy wondered what he could be laughing about, and what fun there could be in frightening a poor little meadow-mouse almost to death.

Later that very same morning, while he was hard at work cutting a new path, he heard footsteps behind him, and turned to see a big, black bird stalking along the little path. He didn't wait for closer acquaintance, but dived into the thick grass, and, as he did so, the big, black bird made a lunge at him, but missed him. It was his first meeting with Blacky the Crow, and he had learned of one more enemy to watch out for.

But most of all he feared Reddy Fox. He never could be quite sure when Reddy was about. Sometimes it would be in broad daylight, and sometimes in the stilly night. The worst of it was,

Reddy seemed to know all about the ways of meadow-mice, and would lie perfectly still beside a little path until an unsuspecting mouse came along. Then there would be a sudden spring, a little squeak cut short right in the middle, and there would be one less happy little worker and playmate. So Tommy learned to look and listen before he started for any place, and then to scurry as fast as ever he could.

Twice Mr. Gopher Snake almost caught him, and once he got away from Billy Mink by squeezing into a hole between some roots too small for Billy to get in. It was a very exciting life, very exciting indeed. He couldn't understand why, when all he wanted was to be allowed to mind his own business and work and play in peace, he must be forever running or hiding for his life. He loved the sweet meadow-grasses and the warm sunshine. He loved to hear the bees humming and the birds singing. He thought the Green Meadows the most beautiful place in all the Great World, and he was very happy when he wasn't frightened; but there was hardly an hour of the day or night that he didn't have at least one terrible fright.

Still, it was good to be alive and explore new places. There was a big rock in front of him right now. He wondered if there was anything to eat on top of it. Sometimes he found the very nicest seeds in the cracks of big rocks. This one looked as if it would not be very hard to scramble up on. He felt almost sure that he would find some

treasure up there.   He looked this way
and that way to make sure no one was
watching.   Then he scrambled up on
the big rock.

For a few minutes, Tommy stared out
over the Green Meadows.   They were
very beautiful.   It seemed to him that
they never had been so beautiful, or the
songs of the birds so sweet, or the Merry
Little Breezes, the children of Old
Mother West Wind, so soft and caress-
ing.   He couldn't understand it all,
for he wasn't a meadow-mouse — just a
barefooted boy sitting on a big stone
that was just made to sit on.

As he looked down, he became aware
of two very small bright eyes watching
him from a little opening in the grass.
He knew them right away.   Of course
he did.   They were the eyes of Danny

*He loved to hear the bees humming
and the birds singing*

Meadow Mouse. They were filled with curiosity, a little doubtful, a little fearful, but tremendously interested. Tommy smiled, and felt in his pocket for some cracker-crumbs. Danny ran away at the first move, but Tommy scattered the crumbs where he could find them, as he was sure to come back.

Tommy stood up and stretched. Then he turned and looked curiously at the stone on which he had been sitting. "I believe it's a real wishing-stone," said he. Then he laughed aloud. "I'm glad I'm not a meadow-mouse, but just a boy!" he cried. "I guess those cows are wondering what has become of me."

He started toward the pasture, and now there was no frown darkening his freckled face. It was clear and good to see, and he whistled as he trampled along. Once he stopped and grinned sheepishly as his blue eyes drank in the beauty of the Green Meadows and beyond them the Green Forest. "And I said there was nothing interesting or exciting going on here! Why, it's the most exciting place I ever heard of, only I didn't know it before!" he muttered. "Gee, I *am* glad I'm not a meadow-mouse, and if ever I throw sticks or stones at one again, I — well I hope I turn into one!"

And though Danny Meadow Mouse, timidly nibbling at the cracker-crumbs, didn't know it, he had one less enemy to be afraid of!

CHAPTER TWO

FROM over in the Green Forest where the silver beeches grow, came a sound which made Tommy stop to listen. For a minute or two all was still. Then it came again, a deep, throbbing sound that began slowly and then grew faster and faster until it ended in a long rumble like distant thunder. Tommy knew it couldn't be that, for there wasn't a cloud in the sky; and anyway it wasn't the season of thunder-storms. Again he heard that deep hollow throbbing grow fast and faster until there was no time between the beats and it became a thunderous rumble; and for some reason which he could not have explained, Tommy felt his pulse beat faster in unison, and a strange sense of joyous exhilaration.

Drum — drum — drum — drum — drum, drum, drum, dr-r-r-r-r-um! The sound beat out from beyond the hemlocks and rolled away through the woods.

"It's an old cock-partridge drumming." Tommy had a way of talking to himself when he was alone. "He's down on that old beech log at the head of the gully. Gee, I'd like to see him! Bet it's the same one that was there last year. Dad says that old log is a reg'lar drumming-log and he's seen partridges drum there lots of times. And yet he doesn't really know how they make all that noise. Says some folks say they

beat the log with their wings, and, because it's hollow, it makes that sound.
Don't believe it, though. They'd
break their wings doing that. Besides,
that old log isn't much hollow anyway,
and I never can make it sound up much
hammering it with a stick; so how could
a partridge do it with nothing but his
wings?

"Some other folks say they do it by
hitting their wings together over their
backs; but I don't see any sense in that,
because their wings are mostly feathers.
And some say they beat their sides to
make the noise; but if they do that, I
should think they'd knock all the wind
out of themselves and be too sore to
move. Bet if I could ever catch ol'
Thunderer drumming, I'd find out how
he does it! I know what I'll do! I'll

go over to the old wishing-stone. Wonder why I didn't think of it before. Then I'll find out a lot."

He thrust his hands into his pockets and trudged up the Crooked Little Path, out of the Green Forest, and over to the great gray stone on the edge of the Green Meadows where once a wish had come true, or had seemed to come true, anyway, and where he had learned so much about the life of Danny Meadow Mouse. As he tramped, his thoughts were all of Thunderer the Ruffed Grouse, whom he called a partridge, and some other people call a pheasant, but who is neither.

Many times had Tommy been startled by having the handsome bird spring into the air from almost under his feet, with a noise of wings that was enough to scare

anybody. It was because of this and the
noise of his drumming that Tommy
called him Thunderer.

With a long sigh of satisfaction, for
he was tired, Tommy sat down on the
wishing-stone, planted his elbows on his
knees, dropped his chin in his hands,
looked over to the Green Forest through
half-closed eyes, and wished.

"I wish," said he, slowly and earnestly, "I could be a partridge." He
meant, of course, that he could be a
grouse.

Just as had happened before when
he had expressed such a wish on the old
wishing-stone, the very instant the
words were out of his mouth, he ceased
to be a boy. He was a tiny little bird,
like nothing so much as a teeny, weeny
chicken, a soft little ball of brown and

yellow, one of a dozen, who all looked alike as they scurried after their little brown mother in answer to her anxious cluck.

Behind them, on the ground, cunningly hidden back of a fallen tree, was an empty nest with only some bits of shell as a reminder that, just a few hours before, it had contained twelve buff eggs. Now Tommy and his brothers and sisters didn't give the old nest so much as a thought. They had left it as soon as they were strong enough to run. They were starting out for their first lesson in the school of the Great World.

Perhaps Tommy thought his mother fussy and altogether a great deal too nervous; but if he did, he didn't say so. There was one thing that seemed to have been born in him, something that as a boy he had to learn, and that was the habit of instant obedience.

It was instinct, which, so naturalists say, is habit confirmed and handed down through many generations. Tommy didn't know why he obeyed. He just did, that was all. It didn't occur to him that there was anything else to do. The idea of disobeying never entered his funny, pretty little head. And it was just so with all the others. Mother Grouse had only to speak and they did just exactly what she told them to.

This habit of obedience on their part took a great load from the mind of Mother Grouse. They hadn't been in the Great World long enough to know, but she knew that there were dangers on every side; and to watch out for and

protect them from these she needed all
her senses, and she couldn't afford to
dull any of them by useless worrying.
So it was a great relief to her to know
that, when she had bidden them hide
and keep perfectly still until she called
them, they would do exactly as she said.
This made it possible for her to leave
them long enough to lead an enemy
astray, and be sure that when she
returned she would find them just where
she had left them.

She had to do this twice on their very
first journey into the Great World.
Tommy was hurrying along with the
others as fast as his small legs could take
him when his mother gave a sharp but
low call to hide.   There was a dried
leaf on the ground close to Tommy.   Instantly he crept under it and flattened

his small self to the ground, closed his
eyes tight, and listened with all his
might.

He heard the whir of strong wings
as Mother Grouse took flight. If he
had peeped out, he would have seen that
she flew only a very little way, and that,
when she came to earth again, there ap-
peared to be something the matter with
her, so that she flopped along instead of
running or flying. But he didn't see
this, because he was under that dead
leaf.

Presently, the ground vibrated under
the steps of heavy feet that all but trod
on the leaf under which Tommy lay,
and frightened him terribly. But he
did not move and he made no sound.
Again, had he peeped out, he would have
seen Mother Grouse fluttering along the

ground just ahead of an eager boy who thought to catch her and tried and tried until he had been led far from the place where her babies were.

Then all was still, so still that surely there could be no danger near. Surely it was safe to come out now. But Tommy didn't move, nor did any of his brothers and sisters. They had been told not to until they were called, and it never once entered their little heads to disobey. Mother knew best.

At last there came a gentle cluck. Instantly Tommy popped out from under his leaf to see his brothers and sisters popping out from the most unexpected places all about him. It seemed almost as if they had popped out of the very ground itself. And there was Mother Grouse, very proud and very fussy, as

she made sure that all her babies were
there.

Later that same day the same thing
happened, only this time there was no
heavy footstep, but the lightest kind of
patter as cushioned feet eagerly hurried
past, and Reddy Fox sprang forward,
sure that Mother Grouse was to make
him the dinner he liked best, and thus
was led away to a safe distance, there
to realize how completely he had been
fooled.

It was a wonderful day, that first day.
There was a great ant-hill which Mother
Grouse scratched open with her stout
claws, exposing ever and ever so many
white things, which were the so-called
eggs of the big black ants, and which
were delicious eating, as Tommy soon
found out.   It was great fun to scramble

for them, and eat and eat until not another one could be swallowed. And when the shadows began to creep through the Green Forest, they nestled close under Mother Grouse in one of her favorite secret hiding-places and straightway went to sleep as healthy children should, sure that no harm could befall them, nor once guessed how lightly their mother slept and more than once shivered with fear, not for herself but for them, as some prowler of the night passed their retreat.

So the days passed and Tommy grew and learned, and it was a question which he did the faster. The down with which he had been covered gave way to real feathers and he grew real wings, so that he was little over a week old when he could fly in case of need. And in that

same length of time, short as it was, he
had filled his little head with knowledge. He had learned that a big sandy
dome in a sunny spot in the woods
usually meant an ants' castle, where he
could eat to his heart's content if only
it was torn open for him.

He had learned that luscious fat
worms and bugs were to be found under
rotting pieces of bark and the litter of
decaying old logs and stumps. He had
learned that wild strawberries and some
other berries afforded a welcome variety
to his bill of fare.

He had learned that a daily bath in
fine dust was necessary for cleanliness
as well as being vastly comforting. He
had learned that danger lurked in the
air as well as on the ground, for a swoop-
ing hawk had caught one of his brothers

who had not instantly heeded his mother's warning.

But most important of all, he had learned the value of that first lesson in obedience, and to trust wholly to the wisdom of Mother Grouse and never to question her commands.

A big handsome grouse had joined them now. It was old Thunderer, and sometimes when he would throw back his head, spread his beautiful tail until it was like a fan, raise the crest on his head and the glossy ruff on his neck, and proudly strut ahead of them, Tommy thought him the most beautiful sight in all the world and wondered if ever he would grow to be half as handsome. While he did little work in the care of the brood, Thunderer was of real help to Mother Grouse in guarding the little

Bugs were to be found under old logs

family from ever-lurking dangers. There was no eye or ear more keen than his, and none more skillful than he in confusing and baffling a hungry enemy who had chanced to discover the presence of the little family. Tommy watched him every minute he could spare from the ever important business of filling his crop, and stored up for future need the things he learned.

Once he ventured to ask Thunderer what was the greatest danger for which a grouse must watch out, and he never forgot the answer.

"There is no greatest danger while you are young," replied Thunderer, shaking out his feathers. "Every danger is greatest while it exists. Never forget that. Never treat any danger lightly. Skunks and foxes and weasels and minks and coons and hawks and owls are equally dangerous to youngsters like you, and one is as much to be feared as another. It is only when you have become full-grown, like me, and then only in the fall of the year, that you will know the greatest danger."

"And what is that?" asked Tommy timidly.

"A man with a gun," replied Thunderer.

"And what is that?" asked Tommy again, eager for knowledge.

"A great creature who walks on two legs and points a stick which spits fire and smoke, and makes a great noise, and kills while it is yet a long distance off."

"Oh!" gasped Tommy. "How is one ever to learn to avoid such a dreadful danger as that?"

"I'll teach you when the time comes," replied Thunderer. "Now run along and take your dust-bath. You must first learn to avoid other dangers before you will be fitted to meet the greatest danger."

All that long bright summer Tommy thought of that greatest danger, and, by learning how to meet other dangers, tried to prepare himself for it. Sometimes he wondered if there really could be any greater danger than those about him every day. It seemed sometimes as if all the world sought to kill him, who was so harmless himself. Not only were there dangers from hungry animals, and robbers of the air, but also from the very creatures that furnished him much of his living—the tribe of insects. An ugly-looking insect, called a tick, with wicked blood-sucking jaws, killed one of the brood while they were yet small, and an equally ugly worm called a bot-worm caused the death of another.

Shadow the Weasel surprised one foolish bird who insisted on sleeping on the ground when he was big enough to know better, and Reddy Fox dined on another whose curiosity led him to move when he had been warned to lie perfectly still, and who paid for his disobedience with his life.   Tommy, not three feet away, saw it all and profited by the lesson.

He was big enough now to act for himself and no longer depended wholly for safety on the wisdom of Mother Grouse and Thunderer.   But while he trusted to his own senses and judgment,

he was ever heedful of their example and
still ready to learn.   Especially did he
take pains to keep near Thunderer and
study him and his ways, for he was wise
and cunning with the cunning of ex-
perience and knowledge.   Tommy was
filled with great admiration for him and
tried to copy him in everything.

Thus it was that he learned that there
were two ways of flying, one without
noise and the other with the thunder
of whirring wings.   Also he learned that
there was a time for each.   When he
knew himself to be alone and suddenly
detected the approach of an enemy, he
often would launch himself into the air
on silent wings before his presence had
been discovered.   But when others of
his family were near, he would burst
into the air with all the noise he could

make as a warning to others. Also, it sometimes startled and confused the enemy.

Thunderer had taught him the trick one day when Reddy Fox had stolen, unseen by Tommy, almost within jumping distance. Thunderer had seen him, and purposely had waited until Reddy was just gathering himself to spring on the unsuspecting Tommy. Then with a splendid roar of his stout wings Thunderer had risen just to one side of the fox, so startling him and distracting his attention that Tommy had had ample time to whir up in his turn, to the discomfiture of Reddy Fox.

So, when the fall came, Tommy was big from good living, and filled with the knowledge that makes for long life among grouse. He knew the best scratching-grounds, the choicest feeding-places according to the month, every bramble-tangle and every brush-pile, the place for the warmest sun-bath, and the trees which afforded the safest and most comfortable roosting places at night.

He knew the ways and the favorite hunting-grounds of every fox, and weasel, and skunk, and coon of the neighborhood, and how to avoid them. He knew when it was safest to lie low and trust to the protective coloring of his feathers, and when it was best to roar away on thundering wings.

The days grew crisp and shorter. The maples turned red and yellow, and soon the woods were filled with fluttering leaves and the trees began to grow bare. It was then that old Thunderer warned

Tommy that the season of greatest danger was at hand. Somehow, in the confidence of his strength and the joy of the splendid tide of life surging through him, he didn't fear this unknown danger as he had when as a little fellow he had first heard of it. Then one day, quite unexpectedly, he faced it.

He and Thunderer had been resting quietly in a bramble-tangle on the very edge of the Green Forest, when suddenly there was the rustle of padded feet in the leaves just outside the brambles. Looking out, Tommy saw what at first he took to be a strange and very large kind of fox, and he prepared to fly.

"Not yet! Not yet!" warned Thunderer. "That is a dog and he will not harm us. But to fly now might be to go straight into that greatest danger, of

which I had told you.   That is the mis-
take young grouse often make, flying
before they know just where the danger
is.   Watch until you see the two-legged
creature with the fire-stick, then follow
me and do just as I do."

The dog was very near now.   In fact,
he had his nose in the brambles and was
standing as still as if turned to stone,
one of his fore feet lifted and pointing
straight at them.   No one moved.
Presently Tommy heard heavy steps,
and, looking through the brambles, saw
the great two-legged creature of whom
Thunderer had told him.

"Now!" cried Thunderer.   "Do as I
do!"   With a great roar of wings he
burst out of the tangle on the opposite
side from where the hunter was, and
flying low, so as to keep the brambles

between himself and the hunter, swerved sharply to the left to put a tree between them, and then flew like a bullet straight into the Green Forest where the trees were thickest, skillfully dodging the great trunks, and at last at a safe distance sailing up over the tops to take to the ground on the other side of a hill and there run swiftly for a way.

Tommy followed closely, doing exactly as Thunderer did. Even as he swerved behind the first tree, he heard a terrible double roar behind him and the sharp whistle of things which cut through the leaves around him and struck the tree behind him. One even nipped a brown feather from his back. He was terribly frightened, but he was unhurt as he joined Thunderer behind the hill.

"Now you know what the greatest
danger is," said Thunderer. "Never fly
until you know just where the hunter is,
and then fly back of a bush or a tree,
the bigger the better, or drop over the
edge of a bank if there is one. Make
as much noise as you can when you get
up. It may startle the hunter so that
he cannot point his fire-stick straight.
If he has no dog, it is sometimes best to
lie still until he has passed and then fly
silently. If there is no tree or other
cover near enough when you first see the
dog, run swiftly until you reach a place
where it will be safe to take wing."

For the next few weeks it seemed as
if from daylight to dark the woods were
filled with dogs and hunters, and
Tommy knew no hour of peace and se-
curity until the coming of night.   Many

a dreadful tragedy did Tommy see when
companions, less cunning than old
Thunderer, were stricken in mid-air and
fell lifeless to the ground. But he,
learning quickly and doing as Thunderer did, escaped unharmed.

At last the law, of which Tommy
knew nothing, put an end to the murder
of the innocents, and for another year
the greatest danger was over. But now
came a new danger. It was the month
of madness. Tommy and all his companions were seized with an irresistible
desire to fly aimlessly, blindly, sometimes in the darkness of night, they
knew not where. And in this mad flight
some met death, breaking their necks
against buildings and against telegraph
wires. Where he went or what he did
during this period of madness, Tommy

never knew; but when it left him as abruptly as it had come, he found himself in the street of a village.

With swift strong wings he shot into the air and headed straight back for the dear Green Forest, now no longer green save where the hemlocks and pines grew. Once back there, he took up the old life and was happy, for he felt himself a match for any foe. The days grew shorter and the cold increased. There were still seeds and acorns and some berries, but with the coming of the snow these became more and more scarce and Tommy was obliged to resort to catkins and buds on the trees. Between his toes there grew little horny projections, which were his snowshoes and enabled him to get about on the snow without sinking in. He learned to dive into the deep soft snow for warmth and safety. Once he was nearly trapped there. A hard crust formed in the night and, when morning came, Tommy had hard work to break out.

So the long winter wore away and spring came with all its gladness. Tommy was fully as big as old Thunderer now and just as handsome, and he began to take pride in his appearance and to strut. One day he came to an old log, and, jumping up on it, strutted back and forth proudly with his fan-like tail spread its fullest and his broad ruff raised. Then he heard the long rolling thunder of another grouse drumming. Instantly he began to beat his wings against the air, not as in flying, but with a more downward motion, and to his great delight there rolled from

under them that same thunder.   Slowly
he beat at first and then faster and faster, until he was forced to stop for breath.
He was drumming!   Then he listened
for a reply.

*Drum — drum — drum — drum —
drum, drum, drum, dr-r-r-r-r-r-rum.*
Tommy's eyes flew open. He was sitting
on the old wishing-stone on the edge of
the Green Meadows.   For a minute he
blinked in confusion.   Then, from over
in the Green Forest, came that sound
like distant thunder, *drum — drum —
drum — drum — drum, drum, drum,
dr-r-r-r-r-r-rum.*

"It's ol' Thunderer again on that
beech log!" cried Tommy.   "And now
I know how he does it.   He just beats
the air.   I know, because I've done it
myself.   Geewhilikens, I'm glad I'm

not really a partridge! Bet I'll never
hunt one after this, or let anybody else
if I can help it.   Isn't this old wishing-
stone the dandy place to learn things,
though!   I guess the only way of really
knowing how birds and animals live and
feel is by being one of 'em.   Somehow
it makes things look all different.   Just
listen to ol' Thunderer drum!   I know
now just how fine he feels.   I'm going
to get Father to put up a sign and stop
all shooting in our part of the Green
Forest next fall, and then there won't be
any greatest danger there."

And Tommy, whistling merrily, started for home.

CHAPTER THREE

WHAT HAPPENED WHEN TOMMY BECAME A MINK

IT was not often that Tommy caught so much as a glimpse of Billy Mink; and every time he did, he had the feeling that he had been smart, very smart indeed. The funny thing is that this feeling annoyed Tommy. Yes, it did. It annoyed him because it seemed so very foolish to think that there was anything smart in just *seeing* Billy Mink. And yet every time he did see him, he had the feeling that he had really done something out of the usual.

Little by little, he realized that it was because Billy Mink himself is so smart,

and manages to keep out of sight so
much of the time, that just seeing him
once in a while gave him the feeling of
being smarter than Billy.

At the same time, he was never quite
sure that Billy didn't intend to be seen.
Somehow that little brown-coated scamp
always seemed to be playing with him.
He would appear so suddenly that
Tommy never could tell just where he
came from. And he would disappear
quite as quickly. Tommy never could
tell where he went. He just vanished,
that was all. It was this that made
Tommy feel that he had been smart to
see him at all.

Now Tommy had been acquainted
with Billy Mink for a long time. That
is to say, he had known Billy by sight.
More than that, he had tried to trap

Billy, and in trying to trap him he had learned some of Billy's ways. In fact, Tommy had spent a great deal of time trying to catch Billy. You see, he wanted that little brown fur coat of Billy's because he could sell it. But it was very clear that Billy wanted that little fur coat himself to wear, and also that he knew all about traps.

So Billy still wore his coat, and Tommy had taken up his traps and put them away with a sigh for the money which he had hoped that that coat would bring him, and with a determination that, when cold weather should come again, he would get it. You see it was summer now, and the little fur coat was of no value then save to Billy himself.

In truth, Tommy would have forgotten all about it until autumn came again had not Billy suddenly popped out in front of him that very morning, while Tommy was trying to catch a trout in a certain quiet pool in the Laughing Brook deep in the Green Forest. Tommy had been sitting perfectly still, like the good fisherman that he was, not making the tiniest sound, when he just seemed to feel two eyes fixed on him. Very, very slowly Tommy turned his head. He did it so slowly that it almost seemed as if he didn't move it at all. But careful as he was, he had no more than a bare glimpse of a little brown animal, who disappeared as by magic.

"It's that mink," thought Tommy, and continued to stare at the spot where he had last seen Billy. The rustle of a leaf almost behind him caused him to

forget and to turn quickly.   Again he
had just a glimpse of something brown.
Then it was gone.   Where, he hadn't
the least idea.   It was gone, that was
all.

Tommy forgot all about trout.   It
was more fun to try to get a good look
at Billy Mink and to see what he was doing and where he was going.   Tommy
remembered all that he had been taught
or had read about how to act when trying
to watch his little wild neighbors and he
did the best he could, but all he got was
a fleeting glimpse now and then which
was most tantalizing.   At last he gave
up and reeled in his fish-line.   Then he
started for home.   All the way he kept
thinking of Billy Mink.   He couldn't
get Billy out of his head.

Little by little he realized how, when

all was said and done, he didn't know
anything about Billy. That is, he didn't
really *know*—he just guessed at things.

"And here he is one of my neighbors,"
thought Tommy. "I know a great deal
about Peter Rabbit, and Chatterer the
Red Squirrel, and Reddy Fox, and a lot
of others, but I don't know anything
about Billy Mink, and he's too smart to
let me find out. Huh! he needn't be so
secret about everything. I'm not going
to hurt him."

Then into Tommy's head crept a
guilty remembrance of those traps. A
little flush crept into Tommy's face.
"Anyway, I'm not going to hurt him
now," he added.

By this time he had reached the great
gray stone on the edge of the Green
Meadows, the wishing-stone. Just as a

matter of course he sat down on the edge
of it.   He never could get by without
sitting down **on** it.

It was a very beautiful scene that
stretched out before Tommy, but,
though he seemed to be gazing out at
it, he didn't see it at all.   He was looking through unseeing eyes.   The fact is,
he was too busy thinking, and his
thoughts were all of Billy Mink.   It
must be great fun to be able to go and
come any hour of the day or night, and
to be so nimble and smart.

"I wish I were a mink," said Tommy,
slowly and very earnestly.

Of course you know what happened
then.   The same thing happened that
had happened before on the old wishing-stone.   Tommy was the very thing
he had wished to be.   He was a mink.

Yes, sir, Tommy was a tiny furry little fellow, with brothers and sisters and the nicest little home, in a hollow log hidden among bulrushes, close by the Laughing Brook and with a big pile of brush near it. Indeed, one end of the old log was under the brush-pile.

That made the very safest kind of a play-ground for the little minks. It was there that Mother Mink gave them their first lessons in a game called "Now-you-see-me-now-you-don't." They thought they were just playing, but all the time they were learning something that would be most important and useful to them when they were older.

Tommy was very quick to learn and just as quick in his movements, so that it wasn't long before he could out-run, out-dodge, and out-hide any of his companions, and Mother Mink began to pay special attention to his education. She was proud of him, and because she was proud of him she intended to teach him all the mink lore which she knew.

So Tommy was the first of the family to be taken fishing. Ever since he and his brothers and sisters had been big enough to eat solid food, they had had fish as a part of their bill of fare, and there was nothing that Tommy liked better. Where they came from, he had never bothered to ask. All he cared about was the eating of them. But now he was actually going to catch some, and he felt very important as he glided along behind his mother.

Presently they came to a dark, deep pool in the Laughing Brook. Mrs. Mink peered into its depths. There was the glint of something silvery down there in the brown water. In a flash Mrs. Mink had disappeared in the pool, entering the water so smoothly as to hardly make a splash. For a moment Tommy saw her dark form moving swiftly, then he lost it. His little eyes blazed with eagerness and excitement as he watched.

Ha! What was that? There was something moving under water on the other side of the pool. Then out popped the brown head of Mrs. Mink and in her teeth was a fat trout. Tommy's mouth watered at the sight. What a feast he would have!

But instead of bringing the fish to him, Mrs. Mink climbed out on the opposite bank and disappeared in the brush there. Tommy swallowed hard

Out popped the brown head of Mrs. Mink

with disappointment.   Could it be that he wasn't to have any of it after all?   In a few minutes Mrs. Mink was back again, but there was no sign of the fish. Then Tommy knew that she had hidden it, and for just a minute a wicked thought popped into his head.   He would swim across and hunt for it.   But Mother Mink didn't give him a chance. Though Tommy didn't see it, there was a twinkle in her eyes as she said,

"Now you have seen how easy it is to catch a fish, I shall expect you to catch all you eat hereafter.   Come along with me to the next pool and show me how well you have learned your lesson."

She led the way down the Laughing Brook, and presently they came to another little brown pool.   Eagerly Tommy peered into it.   At first he saw nothing. Then, almost under him, he discovered a fat trout lazily watching for a good meal to come along. With a great splash Tommy dived into the pool. For just a second he closed his eyes as he struck the water. When he opened them, the trout was nowhere to be seen. Tommy looked very crest-fallen and foolish as he crawled up on the bank, where Mother Mink was laughing at him.

"How do you expect to catch fish when you splash like that?" she asked. Tommy didn't know, so he said nothing. "Now you come with me and practise on little fish first," she continued and led him to a shallow pool in which a school of minnows were at play.

Now Tommy was particularly fond of trout, as all Mink are, and he was

inclined to turn up his nose at minnows.
But he wisely held his tongue and prepared to show that he had learned his
lesson.   This time he slipped into the
water quietly and then made a swift
dash at the nearest minnow. He missed
it quite as Mother Mink had expected
he would.   But now his dander was up.
He would catch one of those minnows if
it took him all the rest of the day!
Three times he tried and missed, but the
fourth time his sharp little teeth closed
on a finny victim and he proudly swam
ashore with the fish.

"Things you catch yourself always
taste best," said Mother Mink. "Now
we'll go over on the meadows and catch
some mice."

Tommy scowled. "I want to catch
some more fish," said he.

"Not the least bit of use for you to try," retorted Mother Mink. "Don't you see that you have frightened those minnows so that they have left the pool? Besides, it is time that you learned to hunt as well as fish, and you'll find it is just as much fun."

Tommy doubted it, but he obediently trotted along at the heels of Mother Mink out onto the Green Meadows. Presently they came to a tiny little path through the meadow grasses. Mother Mink sniffed in it and Tommy did the same. There was the odor of meadow-mouse, and once more Tommy's mouth watered. He quite forgot about the fish. Mother Mink darted ahead and presently Tommy heard a faint squeak. He hurried forward to find Mother Mink with a fat meadow-mouse.

Tommy smacked his lips, but she took no notice. Instead, she calmly ate the meadow-mouse herself.

Tommy didn't need to be told that if he wanted meadow-mouse he would have to catch one for himself. With a little angry toss of his head he trotted off along the little path. Presently he came to another. His nose told him a meadow-mouse had been along that way recently. With his nose to the ground he began to run.

Other little paths branched off from the one he was in. Tommy paid no attention to them until suddenly he realized that he no longer smelled meadow-mouse. He kept on a little farther, hoping that he would find that entrancing smell again. But he didn't, so he stopped to consider. Then he turned and ran back, keeping his nose to the ground. So he came to one of those little branch paths and there he caught the smell of meadow-mouse again. He turned into the little branch path and the smell grew stronger. He ran faster.

Then his quick ears caught the sound of scurrying feet ahead of him. He darted along, and there, running for his life, was a fat meadow-mouse. Half a dozen bounds brought Tommy up with him, whereupon the mouse turned to fight. Now the mouse was big and a veteran, and Tommy was only a youngster. It was his first fight. For just a second he paused at the sight of the sharp little teeth confronting him. Then he sprang into his first fight.

The fierce lust of battle filled him.

His eyes blazed red. There was a
short sharp struggle and then the mouse
went limp and lifeless. Very proudly
Tommy dragged it out to where Mother
Mink was waiting. She would have
picked it up and carried it easily, but
Tommy wasn't big enough for that.

After that Tommy went hunting or
fishing every day. Sometimes the whole
family went, and such fun as they would
have! One day they would hunt frogs
around the edge of the Smiling Pool.
Again they would visit a swamp and dig
out worms and insects. But best of all
they liked to hunt the meadow-mice.

So the long summer wore away and
the family kept together. But as the
cool weather of the fall came, Tommy
grew more and more restless. He
wanted to see the Great World. Some-

times he would go off and be gone two
or three days at a time. Then one day
he bade the old home good-by forever,
though he didn't know it at the time.
He simply started off, following the
Laughing Brook to the Great River, in
search of adventure. And in the joy of
exploring new fields he forgot all about
home.

He was a fine big fellow by this time
and very smart in the ways of the Mink
world. Life was just a grand holiday.
He hunted or fished when he was hungry, and when he was tired he curled up
in the nearest hiding-place and slept.
Sometimes it was in a hollow log or
stump. Again it was in an old rock-pile
or under a heap of brush. When he had
slept enough, he was off again on his
travels, and it made no difference to him

whether it was night or day. He just ate when he pleased, slept when he pleased, and wandered on where and when he pleased.

He was afraid of no one. Once in a while a fox would try to catch him or a fierce hawk would swoop at him, but Tommy would dodge like a flash, and laugh as he ducked into some hole or other hiding-place. He had learned that quickness of movement often is more than a match for mere size and strength. So he was not afraid of any of his neighbors, for those he was not strong enough to fight he was clever enough to elude.

He could run swiftly, climb like a squirrel, and swim like a fish. Because he was so slim, he could slip into all kinds of interesting holes and dark corners, and explore stone and brush piles. In fact he could go almost anywhere he pleased. His nose was as keen as that of a dog. He was always testing the air or sniffing at the ground for the odor of other little people who had passed that way. When he was hungry and ran across the trail of some one he fancied, he would follow it just as Bowser the Hound follows the trail of Reddy Fox. Sometimes he would follow the trail of Reddy himself, just to see what he was doing.

For the most part he kept near water. He dearly loved to explore a brook, running along beside it, swimming the pools, investigating every hole in the banks and the piles of drift stuff. When he was feeling lazy and there were no fish handy, he would catch a frog or two,

When he was feeling lazy, he would catch a frog

or a couple of pollywogs, or a crayfish.

Occasionally he would leave the low land and the water for the high land and hunt rabbits and grouse. Sometimes he surprised other ground birds. Once he visited a farmyard and, slipping into the hen-house at night, killed three fat hens. Of course he could not eat the whole of even one.

Tommy asked no favors of any one. His was a happy, care-free life. To be sure he had few friends save among his own kind, but he didn't mind this. He rather enjoyed the fact that all who were smaller, and some who were larger, than he feared him. He was lithe and strong and wonderfully quick.

Fighting was a joy. It was this as much as anything that led him into a fight with a big muskrat, much bigger than himself. The muskrat was stout, and his great teeth looked dangerous. But he was slow and clumsy in his movements compared with Tommy, and, though he was full of courage and fought hard, the battle was not long. After that Tommy hunted muskrats whenever the notion seized him.

Winter came, but Tommy minded it not at all. His thick fur coat kept him warm, and the air was like tonic in his veins. It was good to be alive. He hunted rabbits in the snow. He caught fish at spring-holes in the ice. He traveled long distances under the ice, running along the edge of the water where it had fallen away from the frozen crust, swimming when he had to, investigating muskrat holes, and now and then surprising the tenant.

Unlike his small cousin, Shadow the Weasel, he seldom hunted and killed just for the fun of killing. Sometimes, when fishing was especially good and he caught more than he could use, he would hide them away against a day of need. In killing, the mink is simply obeying the law of Old Mother Nature, for she has given him flesh-eating teeth, and without meat he could not live. In this respect he is no worse than man, for man kills to live.

For the most of the time, Tommy was just a happy-go-lucky traveler, who delighted in exploring new places and who saw more of the Great World than most of his neighbors. The weather never bothered him. He liked the sun, but he would just as soon travel in the rain. When a fierce snow-storm raged, he

traveled under the ice along the bed of
the nearest brook or river. It was just
the life he had dreamed of as a boy. He
was an adventurer, a freebooter, and all
the world was his. He had no work.
He had no fear, for as yet he had not
encountered man. Hooty the Owl by
night and certain of the big hawks by
day were all he had to watch out for,
and these he did not really fear, for he
felt himself too smart for them.

But at last he did learn fear. It came
to him when he discovered another Mink
fast in a trap. He didn't understand
those strange jaws which bit into the
flesh and held and yet were not alive.
He hid near-by and watched, and he saw
a great two-legged creature come and
take the mink away. Then, cautiously,
Tommy investigated. He caught the

odor of the man scent, and a little chill
of fear ran down his backbone.

But in spite of all his care there came
a fateful day. He was running along a
brook in shallow water when snap! from
the bottom of the brook itself the dreadful jaws sprang up and caught him by a
leg. There had been no smell of man
to give him warning, for the running
water had carried it away. Tommy
gave a little shriek as he felt the dreadful thing, and then — he was just
Tommy, sitting on the wishing-stone.

He stared thoughtfully over at the
Green Forest. Then he shuddered.
You see he remembered just how he had
felt when that trap had snapped on his
leg. "I don't want your fur coat, Billy
Mink," said he, just as if Billy could
hear him. "If it wasn't for traps, you

surely would enjoy life. Just the same I wouldn't trade places with you, not even if I do have to hoe corn just when I want to go swimming!"

And with this, Tommy started for home and the hoe, and somehow the task didn't look so very dreadful after all.

CHAPTER FOUR

TOMMY BECOMES A VERY HUMBLE
PERSON

HELLO, old Mr. Sobersides! Where are you bound for?" As he spoke, Tommy thrust a foot in front of old Mr. Toad and laughed as Mr. Toad hopped up on it and then off, quite as if he were accustomed to having big feet thrust in his way. Not that Tommy had especially big feet. They simply were big in comparison with Mr. Toad. "Never saw you in a hurry before," continued Tommy. "What's it all about? You are going as if you were bound for somewhere in particular, and as if you

had something special on your mind.
What is it, anyway?"

Now of course old Mr. Toad didn't
make any reply. At least he didn't
make any that Tommy heard. If he had,
Tommy wouldn't have understood it.
The fact is, it did look, for all the world,
as if it was just as Tommy had said.
If ever any one had an important
engagement to keep and meant to keep
it, Mr. Toad did, if looks counted anything. Hoppity-hop-hop-hop, hoppity-
hop-hop-hop, he went straight down
toward the Green Meadows, and he
didn't pay any attention to anybody or
anything.

Tommy was interested. He had
known old Mr. Toad ever since he could
remember, and he couldn't recall ever
having seen him go anywhere in particu-

lar. Whenever Tommy had noticed him, he had seemed to be hopping about in the most aimless sort of way, and never took more than a half dozen hops without sitting down to think it over. So it was very surprising to see him traveling along in this determined fashion, and, having nothing better to do, Tommy decided to follow him and find out what he could.

So down the Lone Little Path traveled old Mr. Toad, hoppity-hop-hop-hop, hoppity-hop-hop-hop, and behind him strolled Tommy. And while old Mr. Toad seemed to be going very fast, and was, for him, Tommy was having hard work to go slow enough to stay behind. And this shows what a difference mere size may make.

When they reached the wishing-stone,

Mr. Toad was tired from having hurried so, and Tommy was equally tired from the effort of going slow, so both were glad to sit down for a rest. Old Mr. Toad crept in under the edge of the wishing-stone on the shady side, and Tommy, still thinking of old Mr. Toad, sat down on the wishing-stone itself.

"I wonder," he chuckled, "if he has come down here to wish. Perhaps he'll wish himself into something beautiful, as they do in fairy stories. I should think he'd want to. Goodness knows, he's homely enough! It's bad enough to be freckled, but to be covered with warts — ugh! There isn't a single beautiful thing about him."

As he said this, Tommy leaned over that he might better look at old Mr. Toad, and Mr. Toad looked up at

Tommy quite as if he understood what Tommy had said, so that Tommy looked straight into Mr. Toad's eyes.

It was the first time in all his life that Tommy had ever looked into a toad's eyes. Whoever would think of looking at the eyes of a hop-toad? Certainly not Tommy. Eyes were eyes, and a toad had two of them. Wasn't that enough to know? Why under the sun should a fellow bother about the color of them, or anything like that? What difference did it make? Well, it made just the difference between knowing and not knowing; between knowledge and ignorance; between justice and injustice.

Tommy suddenly realized this as he looked straight into the eyes of old Mr. Toad, and it gave him a funny feeling inside. It was something like that feeling you have when you speak to some one you think is an old friend and find him to be a total stranger. "I — I beg your pardon, Mr. Toad," said he. "I take it all back. You have something beautiful — the most beautiful eyes I've ever seen. If I had eyes as beautiful as yours, I wouldn't care how many freckles I had. Why haven't I ever seen them before?"

Old Mr. Toad slowly blinked, as much as to say, "That's up to you, young man. They're the same two eyes I've always had. If you haven't learned to use your own eyes, that is no fault and no business of mine. If I made as little use of my eyes as you do of yours, I shouldn't last long."

It never before had occurred to Tommy that there was anything par-

ticularly interesting about old Mr.
Toad. But those beautiful eyes—for a
toad's eyes are truly beautiful, so beautiful that they are the cause of the old
legend that a toad carries jewels in his
head — set him to thinking. The more
he thought, the more he realized how
very little he knew about this homely,
common neighbor of the garden.

"All I know about him is that he eats
bugs," muttered Tommy, "and on that
account is a pretty good fellow to have
around. My, but he *has* got beautiful
eyes! I wonder if there is anything else
interesting about him. I wonder if I
should wish to be a toad just to learn
about him, if I could be one. I guess
some of the wishes I've made on this old
stone have been sort of foolish, because
every time I've been discontented **or**

envious, and I guess the wishes have come true just to teach me a lesson. I'm not discontented now. I should say not! A fellow would be pretty poor stuff to be discontented on a beautiful spring day like this! And I don't envy old Mr. Toad, not a bit, unless it's for his beautiful eyes, and I guess that doesn't count. I don't see how he can have a very interesting life, but I almost want to wish just to see if it *will* come true."

At that moment, old Mr. Toad came out from under the wishing-stone and started on down the Lone Little Path. Just as before, he seemed to be in a hurry to get somewhere, and to have something on his mind. Tommy had to smile as he watched his awkward hops.

"I may as well let him get a good

start, because he goes so very slow,"
thought Tommy, and dreamily watched
until old Mr. Toad was just going out
of sight around a turn in the Lone Little
Path.   Then, instead of getting up and
following, Tommy suddenly made up
his mind to test the old wishing-stone.
"I wish," said he right out aloud, "I wish
I could be a toad!"

No sooner were the words out of his
mouth than he was hurrying down the
Lone Little Path after old Mr. Toad,
hop-hop-hoppity-hop, a toad himself.
He knew now just where old Mr. Toad
was bound for, and he was in a hurry, a
tremendous hurry, to get there himself.
It was the Smiling Pool. He didn't
know why he wanted to get there, but he
did.   It seemed to him that he couldn't
get there quick enough.   It was spring,

and the joy of spring made him tingle all
over from the tip of his nose to the tips
of his toes; but with it was a great longing—a longing for the Smiling Pool. It
was a longing very much like homesick-
ness. He felt that he couldn't be really
happy until he got there, and that nothing could or should keep him away from
there.

He couldn't even stop to eat. He
knew, too, that that was just the way old
Mr. Toad was feeling, and it didn't sur-
prise him as he hurried along, hop-hop-
hoppity-hop, to find other toads all
headed in the same direction, and all in
just as much of a hurry as he was.

Suddenly he heard a sound that made
him hurry faster than ever, or at least
try to. It was a clear sweet peep, peep,
peep. "It's my cousin Stickytoes the

Tree-toad, and he's got there before me," thought Tommy, and tried to hop faster. That single peep grew into a great chorus of peeps, and now he heard other voices, the voices of his other cousins, the frogs. He began to feel that he must sing too, but he couldn't stop for that.

At last, Tommy reached the Smiling Pool, and with a last long hop landed in the shallow water on the edge. How good the cool water felt to his dry skin! At the very first touch, the great longing left Tommy and a great content took its place. He had reached *home*, and he knew it.

It was the same way with old Mr. Toad and with the other toads that kept coming and coming from all directions. And the very first thing that many of

them did as soon as they had rested a
bit was — what do you think? Why,
each one began to sing. Yes, sir, a great
many of those toads began to sing! If
Tommy had been his true self instead of
a toad, he probably would have been
more surprised than he was when he discovered that old Mr. Toad had beautiful
eyes. But he wasn't surprised now, for
the very good reason that he was singing
himself.

Tommy could no more help singing
than he could help breathing. Just as
he had to fill his lungs with air, so he had
to give expression to the joy that filled
him. He just *had* to. And, as the most
natural expression of joy is in song,
Tommy added his voice to the great
chorus of the Smiling Pool.

In his throat was a pouch for which

he had not been aware that he had any particular use; now he found out what it was for. He filled it with air, and it swelled and swelled like a little balloon, until it was actually larger than his head; and, though he wasn't aware of it, he filled it in a very interesting way. He drew the air in through his nostrils and then forced it through two little slits in the floor of his mouth. All the time he kept his mouth tightly closed.

That little balloon was for the purpose of increasing the sound of his voice. Later he discovered that he could sing when wholly under water, with mouth and nostrils tightly closed, by passing the air back and forth between his lungs and that throat-pouch.

It was the same way with all the other toads, and on all sides Tommy saw them sitting upright in the shallow water with their funny swelled-out throats, and singing with all their might.   In all the Great World, there was no more joyous place than the Smiling Pool in those beautiful spring days.   It seemed as if everybody sang — Redwing the Black-bird in the bulrushes, Little Friend the Song-sparrow in the bushes along the edge of the Laughing Brook, Bubbling Bob the Bobolink in the top of the near-est tree on the Green Meadows, and the toads and frogs in every part of the Smiling Pool.   But of all those songs there was none sweeter or more expres-sive of perfect happiness than that of Tommy and his neighbor, homely, almost ugly-looking, old Mr. Toad.

Tommy saw them sitting upright in the shallow water

"Toad weather! Perfect Toad weather!"
exclaimed old Mr. Toad

But it was not quite true that everybody sang. Tommy found it out in a way that put an end to his own singing for a little while. Jolly, round, bright Mr. Sun was shining his brightest, and the singers of the Smiling Pool were doing their very best, when suddenly old Mr. Toad cut his song short right in the middle. So did other toads and frogs on both sides of him. Tommy stopped too, just because the others did. There was something fearsome in that sudden ending of glad song.

Tommy sat perfectly still with a queer feeling that something dreadful was happening. He didn't move, but he rolled his eyes this way and that way until he saw something moving on the edge of the shore. It was Mr. Black-snake, just starting to crawl away, and from his mouth two long legs were feebly kicking. One of the sweet singers would sing no more. After that, no matter how glad and happy he felt as he sang, he kept a sharp watch all the time for Mr. Snake, for he had learned that there was danger even in the midst of joy.

But when the dusk of evening came, he knew that Mr. Snake was no longer to be feared, and he sang in perfect peace and contentment until there came an evening when again that mighty chorus stopped abruptly. A shadow passed over him. Looking up, he saw a great bird with soundless wings, and hanging from its claws one of the sweet singers whose voice was stilled forever. Hooty the Owl had caught his supper.

So Tommy learned that not all folk

sing their joy in spring, and that those who do not, such as Mr. Blacksnake and Hooty the Owl, were to be watched out for.

"Too bad, too bad!" whispered old Mr. Toad as they waited for some one to start the chorus again. "That fellow was careless. He didn't watch out. He forgot. Bad business, forgetting; bad business. Doesn't do at all. Now I've lived a great many years, and I expect to live a great many more. I never forget to watch out. We toads haven't very many enemies, and if we watch out for the few we have, there isn't much to worry about. It's safe to start that chorus again, so here goes."

He swelled his throat out and began to sing. In five minutes it was as if nothing had happened at the Smiling Pool.

So the glad spring passed, and Tommy saw many things of interest. He saw thousands of tiny eggs hatch into funny little tadpoles, and for a while it was hard to tell at first glance the toad tadpoles from their cousins, the frog tadpoles. But the little toad babies grew fast, and it was almost no time at all before they were not tadpoles at all, but tiny little toads with tails. Day by day the tails grew shorter, until there were no tails at all, each baby a perfect little toad no bigger than a good-sized cricket, but big enough to consider that he had outgrown his nursery, and to be eager to leave the Smiling Pool and go out into the Great World.

"Foolish! Foolish! Much better

off here. Got a lot to learn before they can take care of themselves in the Great World," grumbled old Mr. Toad. Then he chuckled. "Know just how they feel, though," said he. "Felt the same way myself at their age. Suppose you did, too."

Of course, Tommy, never having been little like that, for he had wished himself into a full-grown toad, had no such memory. But old Mr. Toad didn't seem to expect a reply, for he went right on: "Took care of myself, and I guess those little rascals can do the same thing. By the way, this water is getting uncomfortably warm. Besides, I've got business to attend to. Can't sing all the time. Holidays are over. Think I'll start along back to-night. Are you going my way?"

Now Tommy hadn't thought anything about the matter. He had noticed that a great many toads were leaving the Smiling Pool, and that he himself didn't care so much about singing. Then, too, he longed for a good meal, for he had eaten little since coming to the Smiling Pool. So when old Mr. Toad asked if he was going his way, Tommy suddenly decided that he was.

"Good!" replied old Mr. Toad. "We'll start as soon as it begins to grow dark. It's safer then. Besides, I never could travel in bright, hot weather. It's bad for the health."

So when the Black Shadows began to creep across the Green Meadows, old Mr. Toad and Tommy turned their backs on the Smiling Pool and started up the Lone Little Path. They were not in a hurry now, as they had been

when they came down the Lone Little
Path, and they hopped along slowly,
stopping to hunt bugs and slugs and
worms, for they were very, very hungry. Old Mr. Toad fixed his eyes on a
fly which had just lighted on the ground
two inches in front of him. He sat perfectly still, but there was a lightning-
like flash of something pink from his
mouth, and the fly was gone. Mr. Toad
smacked his lips.

"I don't see how some people get
along with their tongues fastened 'way
back in their throats," he remarked.
"The proper place for a tongue to be
fastened is the way ours are—by the
front end. Then you can shoot it out
its whole length and get your meal every
time. See that spider over there? If I
tried to get any nearer, he'd be gone at

the first move. He's a goner anyway. Watch!" There was that little pink flash again, and, sure enough, the spider had disappeared. Once more old Mr. Toad smacked his lips. "Didn't I tell you he was a goner?" said he, chuckling over his own joke.

Tommy quite agreed with old Mr. Toad. That arrangement of his tongue certainly was most convenient. Any insect he liked to eat that came within two inches of his nose was as good as caught. All he had to do was to shoot out his tongue, which was sticky, and when he drew it back, it brought the bug with it and carried it well down his throat to a comfortable point to swallow. Yes, it certainly was convenient.

It took so much time to fill their stomachs that they did not travel far that night. The next day they spent under an old barrel, where they buried themselves in the soft earth by digging holes with their stout hind feet and backing in at the same time until just their noses and eyes showed at the doorways, ready to snap up any foolish bugs or worms who might seek shelter in their hiding-place. It was such a comfortable place that they stayed several days, going out nights to hunt, and returning at daylight.

It was while they were there that old Mr. Toad complained that his skin was getting too tight and uncomfortable, and announced that he was going to change it. And he did. It was a pretty tiresome process, and required a lot of wriggling and kicking, but little by little the old skin split in places and

Mr. Toad worked it off, getting his hind legs free first, and later his hands, using the latter to pull the last of it from the top of his head over his eyes. And, as fast as he worked it loose, he swallowed it!

"Now I feel better," said he, as with a final gulp he swallowed the last of his old suit. Tommy wasn't sure that he *looked* any better, for the new skin looked very much like the old one; but he didn't say so.

Tommy found that he needed four good meals a day, and filling his stomach took most of his time when he wasn't resting. Cutworms he found especially to his liking, and it was astonishing how many he could eat in a night. Cater-pillars of many kinds helped out, and it was great fun to sit beside an ant-hill

and snap up the busy workers as they
came out.

But, besides their daily foraging,
there was plenty of excitement, as when
a rustling warned them that a snake was
near, or a shadow on the grass told them
that a hawk was sailing overhead. At
those times they simply sat perfectly
still, and looked so much like little
lumps of earth that they were not seen
at all, or, if they were, they were not
recognized. Instead of drinking, they
soaked water in through the skin. To
have a dry skin was to be terribly
uncomfortable, and that is why they
always sought shelter during the sunny
hours.

At last came a rainy day. "Toad
weather! Perfect toad weather!" ex-

claimed old Mr. Toad. "This is the day to travel."

So once more they took up their journey in a leisurely way. A little past noon, the clouds cleared away and the sun came out bright. "Time to get under cover," grunted old Mr. Toad, and led the way to a great gray rock beside the Lone Little Path and crawled under the edge of it. Tommy was just going to follow — when something happened! He wasn't a toad at all—just a freckle-faced boy sitting on the wishing-stone.

He pinched himself to make sure. Then he looked under the edge of the wishing-stone for old Mr. Toad. He wasn't there. Gradually he remembered that he had seen old Mr. Toad disappearing around a turn in the Lone

Little Path, going hoppity-hop-hop-hop, as if he had something on his mind.

"And I thought that there was nothing interesting about a toad!" muttered Tommy. "I wonder if it's all true. I believe I'll run down to the Smiling Pool and just see if that is where Mr. Toad really was going. He must have about reached there by this time.

He jumped to his feet and ran down the Lone Little Path. As he drew near the Smiling Pool, he stopped to listen to the joyous chorus rising from it. He had always thought of the singers as just "peepers," or frogs. Now, for the first time, he noticed that there were different voices. Just ahead of him he saw something moving. It was old Mr. Toad. Softly, very softly, Tommy followed and saw him jump into the shallow water. Carefully he tiptoed nearer and watched. Presently old Mr. Toad's throat began to swell and swell, until it was bigger than his head. Then he began to sing. It was only a couple of notes, tremulous and wonderfully sweet, and so expressive of joy and gladness that Tommy felt his own heart swell with happiness.

"It is true!" he cried. "And all the rest must be true. And I said there was nothing beautiful about a toad, when all the time he has the most wonderful eyes and the sweetest voice I've ever heard. It must be true about that queer tongue, and the way he sheds his skin. I'm going to watch and see for myself. Why, I've known old Mr. Toad all my life, and thought him just a common fellow, when all the time he is just wonderful! I'm glad I've been a toad. Of course there is nothing like being a boy, but I'd rather be a toad than some other things I've been on the old wishing-stone. I'm going to get all the toads I can to live in my garden this summer."

And that is just what Tommy did, with the result that he had one of the best gardens anywhere around. And nobody knew why but Tommy — and his friends, the toads.

Tommy had no intention of doing any more wishing on that old stone, but he did. He just couldn't keep away from it. If you want to know what his wishes were and what more he learned you will find it in the next volume, Tommy's Wishes Come True.